AUTHOR'S NOTE

This story is based on the life of **Lily Parr**, one of many amazingly talented women footballers, who despite great **difficulties**, **prejudice** and **ridicule**, battled to keep women's football going, in the 20th Century. Because they wanted their matches to raise money for charity, they accepted very low pay for playing, and so had to fit their games around long hours doing other jobs. Even when they were banned from football grounds, these women carried on playing wherever they could because they **loved the game** so much. And so now, following the trail they blazed, women's football is played and enjoyed by millions around the world.

This book is for all who have **fought prejudice** to fulfil their **true potential**, and continue to do so.

Trailblazer:

Lily Parr, the Unstoppable Star of Women's Football

An original concept by author Elizabeth Dale
© Elizabeth Dale
Illustrated by Carolina Coroa

MAVERICK ARTS PUBLISHING LTD
Studio 11, City Business Centre, 6 Brighton Road, Horsham,
West Sussex, RH13 5BB, +44 (0)1403 256941
© Maverick Arts Publishing Limited
Published May 2020

A CIP catalogue record for this book
is available at the British Library.

ISBN 978-1-84886-642-3

For Chris Woods,
a brilliant footballer and
inspiring teacher.
- E.D.

For all the girls
running after their
dreams, and for Hugo.
- C.C.

Maverick
publishing

www.maverickbooks.co.uk

TRAILBLAZER

Lily Parr, the Unstoppable Star of Women's Football

Written by
Elizabeth Dale

Illustrated by
Carolina Coroa

When Lily was born in England in 1905, her parents had no idea she would become a football star! But Lily loved playing football and she was very good at it. But there were some that didn't think women should play!

Lily trained hard, often with her brothers. Then, when she was only 14, she started playing for a women's team called **St. Helens Ladies**. Alfred, the manager of **Dick, Kerr Ladies**, saw her and was amazed by her skills.

He offered her, and her teammate Alice, a job in his factory. It had its own women's football team.

Lily would have to move away from home, but it meant playing for one of **the best women's teams** in the area!

FACT:
Many factories had their own football teams. It helped keep the workers healthy and happy.

Working in the factory was hard!
But the team were one big family, living
for the evenings and weekends when they
had matches – against **men and women!**

Go Lily!

Lily played brilliantly in any position but usually played outside-left. No one in the country, not even a man, had a more **powerful** shot than her.

FACT:
Lily was very tall for her age and exceptionally fit. She was left-footed.

Some men didn't like being beaten by a women's team. One goalie challenged Lily,
"No woman can beat me!
Bet you can't score a penalty."
"Just watch me!" said Lily.

Lily kicked

Dick, Kerr Ladies became the best team in the country and represented England, beating international teams at home and abroad.

Alice was a great **captain**,

Jennie's **ball control** was brilliant,

FACT:
Their games were so popular, they raised £140,000 for charity - worth nearly several million pounds today.

Florrie was a **top** goal-scorer...

...and Lily was amazing **everywhere** on the pitch.

Crowds flocked to see them
wherever they played.

On December 26th 1920, 53,000 people squeezed into a stadium to watch them play Lily's old team, St. Helens Ladies, with another 14,000 stuck outside.

Let us in!

FACT:
This was the largest crowd that had ever watched a women's game in England.

But, in 1921, the English Football Association **banned** women's teams from playing on all their grounds.

They made lots of excuses.

It is too much for a woman's body.

It is most unsuitable for females.

We should not encourage them.

WOMEN AND FOOTBALL
The council of the Football Association has prohibited the use on its grounds by women's teams, and has expressed its strong opinion that the game of football is quite unsuitable for women.

Did that **stop** Lily and her friends?

No way!

"We'll play even if we have to play on ploughed fields," said their manager, Alfred.
"We play for the **love of the game** and we are determined to carry on," said Alice.

WOMEN'S FOOTBALL BANNED

So they played on village greens and open spaces.
Everywhere they could.

But not many people could watch them there.

Alfred came up with a plan. They would go to **Canada!**

But...

So they went to **the United States.**

There weren't many women's teams in America, so they played against top men's division teams too. They still **won** or **drew** most of their matches.

Lily was the **star player**! She certainly made the headlines:

Daily ⬛ Post

LILY - THE MOST BRILLIANT FEMALE PLAYER IN THE WORLD!

Women's Soccer: Meet the best players

FACT: In the United States they call football 'soccer'.

ENGLISH W MEN BEAT U.S. O MP RACE - WITH UT

But despite all their success...

Back home, the FA **still** banned women from using their grounds.
But they were unstoppable and played wherever they could.

In fact, Lily ended up playing football for **31 years!**
The power of her shots was legendary, her ball skills
were amazing – she was a true football star.

FACT
It wasn't until 1971
that the ban was
finally lifted, 50 years
after it had first been
introduced!

Today, thanks to women like Lily and her teammates, women's football is growing in popularity around the world.

In 2019, the **first statue of a woman footballer** was revealed in the National Football Museum in Manchester.

FACT
Lily was one of the greatest goal-scorers in history, netting nearly 1,000 goals in her career and setting up many more.

That statue was of **Lily!**

Lily's name has gone down in
history as a real...

FOOTBALL TIMELINE

1700s
Women's teams play against each other in the Scottish Highlands, and men went to choose their brides!

1895
The first official women's football match in England – London North beat London South 7-1.

1920
In one of the earliest recognised women's internationals, *Dick, Kerr Ladies*, representing England, beat France 4-0. They then toured France, playing local teams.

1921
The English FA bans women from playing on Football League grounds.

1971
The FA lifts its ban. An England women's team plays in the Mexico World Cup, watched by 80,000 people. Back home, instead of praise they're all given a 3 month ban for taking part!

1991
In England, a national league is formed with 24 clubs and the first official FIFA Women's World Cup is held.

2002
The FA announces that football has become the top sport for girls and women to play in England.

2019
1.12 billion T.V. viewers watch the Women's World Cup tournament. The final between the United States and The Netherlands is watched live by 82.18 million viewers, with 263 million viewers watching it overall.